Horizons

Mike's Bike

Horizons
Phonics and Reading K
Reader 2

Author: Pollyann O'Brien, M.A.

Editor: Alan L. Christopherson, M.S.

Illustrations: Karen Eubanks, B.A.
Dawn Tessier, B.A.

Alpha Omega Publications • Chandler, Arizona

1

Printed in the United States of America

ISBN 0-7403-0142-X

A Note to Teachers and Parents

The Horizons Kindergarten Phonics Readers are to be used as a companion to the Horizons Kindergarten Phonics Student Workbooks. For each lesson in the Student Workbooks there is a corresponding story in the Readers. The story will illustrate and demonstrate the primary concept of the lesson. Most kindergarten students should not be expected to read these stories independently. The stories include a mixture of simple short-vowel words and more complex multi-syllable or long-vowel words. The teacher or parent should read the stories to the student, pausing where appropriate, to allow the student to sound out and read the words they have covered in the lessons. As the student's vocabulary increases, the teacher or parent is encouraged to repeat the Reader stories in a cyclic fashion. For example; on the day "x" is covered (Lesson 26) both the "x" story and the "short a" story (Lesson 1) can be read.

It is important to ask questions both before and after reading the story. Talk about things to look for or to expect in the story based upon the title or the illustrations. Comprehension questions are included at the end of each story beginning with Lesson 27.

The ability to sound out and read words varies with each individual student. They are in the early stages of learning a skill that they will continue to develop for the rest of their lives. So, have fun, enjoy the stories and keep in mind that it is not necessary that every student sound out and read every word.

Table of Contents

Lesson #   Title   Page

41.   Dick's Bike Ride 8

42.   Drake's Drawing 10

43.   A Tube for Floating 12

44.   Jake's Bike 14

45.   Shine 17

46.   Trix Does Tricks 20

47.   Fishing 23

48.   Jane's Cake 28

49.   A Home for Old Rove 30

50.   A Birthday Hike for Greg . 33

51.   Glen and the Sand Dollars . 36

Lesson #	Title	Page
52.	Who Spilled the Milk?	40
53.	The Chimps	44
54.	Dopey's Home	46
55.	Brute, the Mule	50
56.	Brent, the Magic Man	52
57.	Red Roses for Rose	55
58.	The Ant Hill	58
59.	Ring the Bell	62
60.	A Skunk Can Stink	64
61.	The Fun Hunt	67
62.	Scamp, the Tresure Hunter	70

Lesson #	Title	Page
63.	Fisk Has a Job	73
64.	Tramp	76
65.	Who Yelled for Help?	78
66.	Tim Gets Big	80
67.	Hank, the Jester	84
68.	Stan's Big Pants	86
69.	Planting Time	89
✓70.	Spud Does Tricks	92
✓71.	A Train Ride	94

Lesson #	Title	Page
72.	The Snail Trail	97
73.	Dan Learns to Print	99
74.	A Ride On a Sled	102
75.	Smell the Roses	106
76.	What is that Noise?	109
77.	The Fuzzy Runt	112
78.	A Neat Chain	116
79.	Pee Wee	118
80.	The Quilt	121

DICK'S BIKE RIDE

Mike was ten years old. He got a new red bike. It was for his birthday. He had a big smile on his face.

Dick was six years old. He did not smile. He just sat and sat. He said, "Mike gets all the fun. I wish I could ride his bike."

Mike said, "Come here, Dick. Put a smile on your face. Look happy. Then you can ride my bike. I will share my bike with you."

"Thanks, Mike. This is a nice bike. I like to ride your bike," said Dick. "I am happy that you would share your bike."

The bike was fun to ride. It was fun for Mike and fun for Dick. Mike said, "It was fun to share the bike with Dick."

How old was Mike?
What did he get for his birthday?
How old was Dick?
What did Mike do for Dick to make him happy?

DRAKE'S DRAWINGS

Drake would drift off to sleep thinking about how he liked to draw. Every night he dreamed about his pictures. He liked to draw pictures of dogs the best. He made pictures of dogs in a dress; dogs in a drag race; dogs in a draped window. He drew pictures of dogs all the time. Sometimes Mom had to drag him away from his drawing to have dinner.

Drake would look for other things to draw when his Dad took him for a drive. Drake's best friend, Frank, liked to draw pictures of people. As they were driving around, Drake and Frank talked about their artwork. Frank's best picture was of a boy playing a drum in a band. Drake said, "I know what would be fun to do. Let us put our pictures together. You can draw the drum and I will draw my dog playing the drum."

What were Drake's dreams every night?
What did he like to draw the best?
What did Frank like to draw?
What did Drake think would be fun to do?

A TUBE FOR FLOATING

Floyd yelled, "School is out. It is time to go to the lake for fun."

Fred yelled, "Right! School is out! It is time for tents, floating on the tubes, and having a picnic."

The boys got the tent and put it up. They put up their family flag and started a bon-fire. They were hungry and wanted to have something to eat before they went for a walk up the path. The flames on the bonfire were getting hot. "Get out the hotdogs," said Floyd. "The flames are just right for roasting. We are ready for a picnic."

When the boys had finished their hotdogs, they started up the flat path. It was just a short trip to the lake. Floyd had put two rubber tubes in the van so they could use them in the lake. The boys tossed the tubes in the water and jumped in after them. What a lazy day this was! They could float on the tubes all across the lake. This was just what the boys wanted the day school was out.

When did the boys go on their trip?
What were they going to eat?
What did they do after they ate their picnic lunch?
What did they use to help keep them floating?

JAKE'S BIKE

This was a big day for Jake. It was his sixteenth birthday and he was excited. This was the day for the big party. Nine of his best friends were going to be there. Mom and Dad had told him he would get a trail bike for his birthday. He was excited!

Jake had a job at the Super Market. He had a job as one of the 'bag boys'. He did a fine job. But this afternoon he was not quite ready for work. The lines in the store were so long. The people were so slow. He was so excited to get home.

At last Jake was done. His
boss gave him his paycheck
with a bonus. Jake had a roll
of one hundred dimes all tied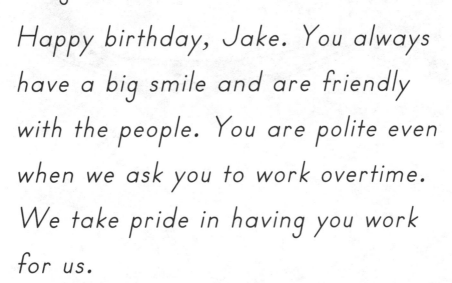
up in a red ribbon as a bonus.
The tag on it said:

> *Happy birthday, Jake. You always*
> *have a big smile and are friendly*
> *with the people. You are polite even*
> *when we ask you to work overtime.*
> *We take pride in having you work*
> *for us.*
>
> *Best wishes,*
> *The Manager*

Jake was so happy and excited, he could hardly wait to get home and show the kids. This made it all worth while.

How old was Jake?
Why was Jake so excited?
Who gave him the bonus?
How much did he get?

SHINE

A long, long, long time ago, there were nine horses on Spade's ranch. One of the horses was very special. Spade called him "Shine".

Shine was the only horse that was all white. He did not whine when Spade wanted him to work. Shine did not seem to get tired. He did not shake or stomp around when Spade put sacks of shale on his back. He stood still when Spade tied blankets with twine on his back. He liked to work.

The other horses fussed and whined. They did not like to work. Spade said, "I am going to do something special for Shine. He is my very special white horse. When he does something good, I will paint a black line on his side."

Shine kept working and Spade kept painting lines on him. Soon Shine had ninety-nine stripes on his sides and legs. He had black lines on his spine. He had a black line on his nose.

Spade said, "Shine is such a fine horse. He is all white with black stripes. He does not shine as much as he used to. I will have to give him a new name."

Can you guess what kind of a zoo animal Shine looked like? Can you think of a better name for Shine?

How many horses did Spade have on his ranch?
What kind of a worker was Shine?
What were the other horses like?
Why did Spade paint black stripes on Shine?
Did you think of a good name for Shine?

TRIX DOES TRICKS

Jim went to a pet store to pick out a pet. He said, "I think I want a dog. I do not want a cat or a fish."

Jim looked at all the pets. He saw slick, black cats, pink fish, and lots of puppies. Then he saw a dog called Trix.

"She is the one I want," said Jim. "She has a thick, black coat."

"Trix is a very smart dog," said the man at the store. "I click my fingers and she comes to me. I think you can train her to do tricks. That is why I named her 'Trix'."

Jim trained Trix to bring a stick back. Then she would sit up with it still in her mouth. Trix learned how to stretch like a cat. Best of all, Trix learned how to hold a bit of meat on her nose until Jim clicked his fingers and said, "OK, Trix, you can have it!"

Trix was a good dog for Jim. He said, "Trix is a very good name for this tricky dog."

Where did Jim get Trix?
What kind of pets did Jim see at the pet store?
Who named the dog "Trix"?
What tricks could Trix do?
What was her best trick?

FISHING

Mom and Dad took Meg with them to the pond to go fishing. Meg had never gone fishing before. She did not know how to do it.

Dad was putting bait on his hook. Meg said, "Oh, Dad, what are you doing?"

"I have to put worms on my hook before the fish will start biting," said Dad.

"Oh, yuck! I am glad I am not a fish and have to start eating worms!" said Meg.

Dad said, "Yes, I am glad you are not a fish, too. Here is your pole. Now you can go fishing just like we will be doing."

Mom cast her line into the water. The fish started biting. She pulled one in. That was her first fish. Soon she got three more fish.

Dad cast his line into the water. A fish started biting Dad's hook. He pulled it in. That was the way the morning started. Before long Dad had six fish.

Meg cast her line into the water. No fish were biting on her hook. She cast it into the water again. She still did not catch any fish.

Meg said, "I am going to leave my pole here in the water. I think Spud and I will play with my ball." She tossed the ball into the air and was waiting for Spud to catch it and bring it back to her.

Dad yelled, "Meg, you have a fish on your hook. Look! Your cork is bobbing up and down. Come and start catching fish with us."

Meg ran back and was trying to pull her line out of the water. The fish kept swim— ming. It was trying to get away. Meg kept pulling harder.

Dad yelled, "Start reeling it in. You have got a big one."

Meg started reeling in the line. She lifted the pole and there was her fish. "It is a big one," she yelled. "I think I like fishing now."

Dad said, "Maybe we got more fish, but you got the biggest one. You are going to be good at fishing."

How did Meg get to the lake?
How many fish did Dad get?
How many fish did Mom get?
What size fish did Meg get?

JANE'S CAKE

Jane said, "I made a cake. I can take the cake to the bake sale. They will race to get my cake. I am sure everyone will like it."

"Oh no," said Jake. "I am sorry, Jane. I came and saw the cake. I ate the cake. Your cake will not ever get to the cake sale."

"Oh, Jake," said Jane. "I will have to bake another cake. I hope I will not be late."

Jake said, "When you bake it, I will take it to the cake sale for you. That will help you a lot."

"I am not so sure that is a good plan, Jake. I better take the cake to the sale myself. Then I will be sure they have a cake."

Who baked a cake?
What was she going to do with it?
What happened to the cake?
Who took the new cake to the sale?

29

A HOME FOR OLD ROVE

James lived with his mom and dad on a ranch.

He did not have any brothers or sisters. He was alone so much of the time.

James said, "I want a dog. I want a dog so we can play together. We could have fun."

Mom and Dad took James to the dog kennel.

James looked at all the dogs in the pens and kennels. He saw a little tan dog. He said, "No, I do not want that one."

30

James saw a big black dog. "No, not that dog," said James.

Then he saw Old Rove. Old Rove was alone. Old Rove looked sad. He seemed to want a home.

James put his hand out to old Rove. Old Rove licked his hand. James said, "Old Rove is the dog for me." Old Rove went home with James.

James fixed good food and lots of bones for Old Rove.

They played together and were happy.

This was good for James and it was a good home for Old Rove.

Where did James live?
What did James want?
Which dog did James get?
What did James to for Old Rove?

A BIRTHDAY HIKE FOR GREG

Dad said, "Happy birthday, Greg. You are nine years old today. This year you have to hike for your birthday surprise." Dad always had a good surprise for Greg.

"Your birthday surprise is at the end of this rope," said Dad. "Just hang on to the tie of this rope and hike."

The rope led Greg to a pile of rocks past the green grass. There was no surprise there. Greg went with the rope around all five big pine trees in the grove. There was no surprise there.

The rope led Greg to the grill. Still there was no surprise.

Greg said, "Dad, are you sure there is a surprise, or is this just a joke?"

Dad said, "Just keep going. You will be getting there soon."

The rope led Greg to the side of a wide pipe. Inside the pipe was Greg's surprise. It was a new red bike. It was just the right size.

Greg said, "Thanks, Dad. I like it. I like it. I like it. I love it." This was the best birthday surprise Greg had ever had. He said, "I like to hike for a surprise like this."

How old was Greg?
Where did Greg go first?
Where did he go next?
Where did Greg find his surprise?

GLEN AND THE SAND DOLLARS

"Let us go to the sand," said Glen. "This would be a great day for it."

"That is a good idea," said Dad. "I would be glad to, but I have to wax the van first.

"I will help, Dad," said Glen. "I like to work on the van." Glen put on a pair of gloves and started to work. "Look here, Dad. Something is stuck on the bumper."

Dad took a look. "I must have spilled some glue on it when I was working last week," he said. "We will have to get some glass wax to fix that."

Glen and Dad took a look at the van. It looked good. "OK, we are ready to go now," said Dad.

Glen and Dad dug in the sand and played in the water. Glen said, "Dad, look what I found. I have ten sand dollars and a bunch of pretty shells."

Dad said, "I like your shells, but I like your sand dollars the best. You have been a good worker today. How would you like a trade trick?"

Glen's grin was from cheek to cheek. "What is your trade trick?"

Dad said, "I will trade you five of your sand dollars for five of my real dollars. Is it a trade?"

"Great," yelled Glen. "Five of my sand dollars for five of your real dollars is a good trade. I will do it."

Where did Glen want to go?
What did Dad have to do to the van?
How many sand dollars did Glen find?
What was the trade trick?

WHO SPILLED THE MILK?

"Who made this spot on the rug?" asked Mom. "I spent all morning with a broom and dust cloth. Now just look at this!"

Spencer came to look at the spot on the rug. "I do not know, Mom. I have been in my room. I have to study my spelling."

"Just look there," said Mom. "There is a glass on the rug. It looks like milk was spilled."

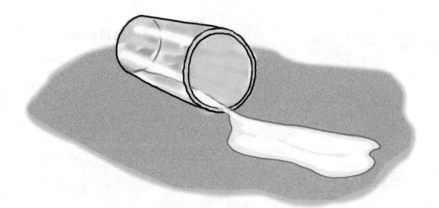

"Oh, oh!" said Spencer.
"Woops! I had a glass of milk
in here and I forgot to take it to
the kitchen. I will bet Spot
pushed it over when he was
chasing that spool of thread on
a string. I will go check."
Spencer went to look for Spot.

"Come here, Spot. Come here, Kitty," said Spencer. Spot was hiding under the bed

licking his lips. "You still have a
speck of milk on your lips, Spot.
Now we know who spilled the milk."

What had happened to the rug?
Who found the spot?
What had Spencer been doing?
Who spilled the milk?

THE CHIMPS

It was fun to watch Chad and Chet at the zoo. Chad was a big chimp who swang from branch to branch. He had long arms and legs and they seemed to stretch anywhere he wanted to jump or swing.

Chet was the little chimp. He watched Chad as he swang from branch to branch. He tried it, too, but his arms did not stretch that far.

Chad would beat his chest and swing

again. Then he would sit and scratch his chin and laugh at Chet.

Chet scratched his chin and watched Chad once more. Chet tried again. This time he checked out branches that were not so far away. He stretched out his long arms and legs and hung on the branch.

Chad and Chet put on a good show for the people at the zoo.

What kind of animals were Chad and Chet?
Where did they live?
Who was the bigger one of the two?
Why could Chet not swing as far as Chad?

DOPEY'S HOME

A long time ago there was a bunch of wild horses. The ranchers said they would give the horses a home. They picked out nine of the biggest and best.

There was one little pony. They did not want him and called him "Dopey". Dopey bumped into stones. He fell in holes. He broke branches from trees. Dopey came along with the others anyway. He ran fast to try to keep up with the bunch of big horses. Dopey was too slow. He got lost. That was no joke. Dopey did not have a home.

At last Dopey came to a park in a town. There were some kids playing. They saw Dopey and said, "A pony! We can take a ride."

Dopey gave all the kids a
ride. Then it was time to go
home. Dopey walked beside
Rose and Dave. Rose said,
"I think I will ride Dopey to
my house."

Dave said, "You can ride Dopey to your house. Then I will ride him the rest of the way to my house. I am going to give Dopey a home.

Now Dopey does not feel alone. Dopey is happy. He has a new home.

Why did the ranchers not take Dopey with them?
Where did Dopey meet Dave and Rose?
Who was going to give Dopey a home?
How does Dopey feel now that he has a new home?

BRUTE, THE MULE

Luke lives on a ranch.

It is a huge ranch.

Luke's dad has many horses on the ranch.

He also has a huge mule named "Brute".

Brute is a huge mule, but he is tame.

Dad has trained Brute to be a good saddle mule.

Luke is good to Brute.

Brute likes Luke and lets him ride on his back.

Where does Luke live?
What size is Brute?
How has Dad trained Brute?
What does Luke do with Brute?

BRENT, THE MAGIC MAN

Brent is a magic man. He does lots of magic tricks. He has a magic cube. It is like a big box.

Brent has a magic crank and a stick on the box. He clamps his hands around the crank and then grabs a drape over it. Presto! Out comes a drum.

Then Brent waves his hands and a green frog brushes by his hat. The frog croaks, "Kerr – upp! Kerr – upp!"

Brent put the magic stick on the cube. A little blue bird fluttered close to his hand. Just as Brent started to catch it, the bird was gone.

Brent will not tell anyone how he does his magic. That is his secret.

What does Brent do?
What was the first trick he did?
What color was the frog?
How does Brent do his magic tricks?

RED ROSES FOR ROSE

Rose was always singing. She could sing high notes. She could sing low notes. She had music in her bones.

One time the school had a dress-up party. All of the kids wore funny hats and pants and masks.

Frank dressed like a cat and did some high jumps. No one knew who he was. Bret dressed like a cowboy and tossed ropes around. Beth dressed like a rabbit. She hopped across the classroom. No one knew who the rabbit and the cowboy were.

At last someone moved on stage in a red velvet robe. She had a long red wig. Her face was painted with a big wide smile. "Who is that?" they asked. Then Rose began to sing.

Everyone yelled, "That is Rose. No one can ever hope to sing like Rose."

Rose won the prize. They gave her some red roses. The note with the roses said, 'RED ROSES FOR ROSE. ROSE IS A WINNER.'

Where was the dress-up party held?
How did Frank dress, and what did he do?
What trick did Beth do?
How did Rose dress, and what did she do?
What did they give Rose?

THE ANT HILL

Brant and Dad went to the pond. They were going to swim and play in the sand. Dad put up the tent and Dan went to play.

As he was going to the sand, he saw a pile of dirt that looked like a little hill. He bent over and put his hand on it. He bent over and looked again. The ants were all over his hand and arm.

"Dad, come and look at this bunch of bugs. They are all over my hand."

Dad said. "Those are little black ants. Here, we will brush them off of you. Those ants were doing their work. When you put your hand in their anthill, they sent them for help."

"There must be a million of them," said Brant.

"Yes, there are millions of them. They all live together in

their colony. Each one has its own task to do and that is all it does. Some clean the colony and mend any holes in it. Others take care of the baby ants. Some are the band of food-ants. Others are the cop-ants and send a S.O.S. if something gets in the way."

"Do not they ever trade jobs?" asked Brant.

"I do not think so," said Dad. "How would you like to have me get you an ant farm? They fix them in a glass box so you can watch them work. Would you like that?"

"That would be good," said Brant... "But for today, I think I will let them work, and I will play in the sand."

Where did Dad and Brant go?
Where did Brant find the anthill?
What is the name of the place where ants live?
What was Brant going to do while the ants worked?

RING THE BELL

Everyone was waiting. Why did the parade not begin? When will it start?

The posters were ready to hang! All the hands were waving! The flags were flying! The band was ready to march in the parade. Why did they not start? All the hands clapped. People yelled, "Let us get started. Let us get started."

Then the bell rang six times. The parade was ready to start. That is why they were waiting. The bell had to ring six times. The band came first playing their marching songs. All the hands clapped for them.

Some men sang songs about the flag. The band played and played. The men sang and sang. All the hands clapped for them.

Then the gang came out and did their flips and handstands. Then all the hands clapped even more for the gang that did their tricks. This was a good parade.

Why did the parade not start at first?
How many times did the bell ring?
Who came out first in the parade?
What songs did the men sing?
Who got the most clapping hands?

A SKUNK CAN STINK

Frank jumped out of his bunk one day. "Come get out of bed, Hank. This is the day we have to yank out the trash and take it to the dump."

The boys filled the boxes with the junk they did not want any more. "Down to the dump with the junk. Down to the dump with the junk. Down to the dump with the junk," Hank kept singing.

"I will conk you on the head if you keep on singing," said Frank. "Let us get away from this dump – and fast as a wink."

64

"What is that bad smell?" asked Hank. "This is the worst gunk I have ever smelled. This is the worst gunk I have ever smelled. This is the worst gunk I have ever smelled." Hank kept on singing.

"Oh, oh," said Frank. "I know what it is. Do you see that little black animal with the white stripe down its back? It is a skunk and we better get out of here – and faster than a wink."

"Good idea," said Hank. "That stinking skunk is a stinker. He stunk up the dump and the junk with his stink. Would you like to have me sing that song for you?"

"Thanks, but NO THANKS," said
Frank. "I do not need that song. It stinks."

Where did Frank sleep?
Where did he have to go?
What did they see when they got there?
What kind of song did Hank sing?

THE FUN HUNT

Glen and Brad loved to go to Grandpa's house. Fun things were always planned for them.

Grandpa said, "We are going to have a fun hunt. He gave the boys a note. The first note said, LOOK UNDER THE SINK IN THE KITCHEN FOR ANOTHER NOTE.

The kitchen note said, CHECK BEHIND THE SONG BOOKS IN THE DEN.

The third note in the den said,
THINK WHERE YOU GO TO SEND
A LETTER. YOU HAVE ANOTHER
NOTE THERE.

The boys went to the mailbox. The
note said, THIS NOTE WILL SEND
YOU TO THE TENT.
By now the boys were
running even faster.

They found the note
in the tent. It said,
YOU HAVE

CHECKED OUT OK ON YOUR FUN HUNT. COME TO MY ROCKING CHAIR. I HAVE SOMETHING FOR YOU.

The boys ran in the house where Grandpa was sitting in his rocking chair. "Here are twenty dollar bills for each of you. I hope you have had fun reading your notes."

"Thanks, Grandpa," said both the boys. "This was a fun hunt for sure. Thanks for the money, too."

Where did Grandpa hide the first note?
Where did the kitchen note tell the boys to look next?
What was the next place the boys looked?
What did the third note say?
Where was the last place they had to go?
What was Grandpa's surprise?

SCAMP, THE TREASURE HUNTER

Scott had a pup named "Scamp". Scott would run to the brush to hide from his pup. Scamp was only six months old, but he knew how to scout for Scott.

Scott was on his scooter going down the street. Scamp was just in back of him. Scott would try to go faster than Scamp, but Scamp always kept up with him.

One day Scott took Scamp for a walk in the desert. Scamp ran way ahead of Scott. Soon Scamp started barking and running back to Scott. Then Scamp would run way ahead again and bark more.

When Scott got close to Scamp, he saw the skull of an ox. The skull must have been there for a long time. It had no skin on its bones. Its scalp had no hair. Just the bones were there. Scamp stood beside the skull and barked. It was if he wanted Scott to tell him what a good hunter he was.

Scott said, "Yes, Scamp, you are a good treasure hunter. But who wants to have a skull for a treasure?"

How old was Scamp?
What did Scamp do when Scott hid from him?
What did Scamp find in the desert?
Did Scott want the treasure?

FISK HAS A JOB

Fisk said, "I want a job this summer. I want to go to work on a farm if I can." Fisk had visited his friend, Brad, last summer and he had fun on the farm.

Mom said, "It gets so hot on the farm. It does not cool off until dusk some days. The tasks are too hard for you."

"Oh, Mom," said Fisk. "I am not a baby." I like to do all the farm tasks. I like to milk the cows. I like to take food to the sheep. I like to feed the chickens. Best of all, I like to ride horseback to herd the horses back into the barn."

Fisk went to see his friend, Brad, and his dad. "Do you have some farm tasks I can do," he asked.

"Yes, we do," said Brad's dad. "We were looking for someone to work for us, and you came just at the right time. We have a list of tasks we need help to do. This is the best time. We are glad to have you here."

Where did Fisk want to work?
What were some of the things Fisk liked to
do on the farm?
What did he like to do the best?
Where did Fisk go to work?

TRAMP

Gramps lived on a farm all alone. His wife had died and he was lonesome. Gramps wanted to get a dog so he would have something to keep him company.

There was a stray puppy that came by Gramps farm. "Right now," said Gramps, "you look like a tramp. You are muddy and dirty and you do not smell too good!"

Gramps took the puppy to the pump and gave him a good bath. "I am going to keep you," said Gramps, "and 'Tramp' is going to be your name."

Tramp looked much better, but he was still a fuzzy puppy with big brown eyes. When

Tramp started to jump over things, he stumbled. He bumped into the lamp. He bumped into the tub. He bumped into everything.

Gramps said, "You are a little fuzzy puppy now, Tramp. When you get older, you will still be big and fuzzy. But when you are big, you will not bump into everything."

Why did Gramps want a dog?
What did Gramps do for Tramp when he first saw him?
What did Tramp do?

WHO YELLED FOR HELP?

"Help! Help!" yelled Ken. "I fell and I need help. I am at the back of the camp and my leg hurts."

Jack and Ted heard Ken's yelp for help. They ran to him and helped him back to camp. Ken's Mom and Dad were at the camp. They took him home so he could see a doctor.

The doctor said, "Ken, you must be kept in bed for ten days. It will take ten days for your leg to mend."

Mom and Dad kept Ken as happy as they could. Jack and Ted came to see him. That made Ken happy.

Pat left a letter for him. Sam put a pen on his desk. Benny sent him a red vest. Ken had many pals. Ken felt better each day. Soon his leg got well.

Why did Ken yell, "Help! Help!"?
Where was Ken when he fell?
Where did Mom and Dad take Ken?
How long did Ken have to stay in bed?
What did his friends do to make him happy?

TIM GETS BIG

Tim was a little kid. He was just six. He had been sick. Tim said, "I wish I were big. I wish I were as big as Mick." Tim pouted and started to sulk.

Mick was ten. He could lift a pig. He could pick up a big tub of fish. He could put up a tent. Mack had big fists. He was a big kid. Mick was a hulk.

Tim said, "I wish I were as big as Mick. I do not want to be sick."

"Sip your milk," said Mick. "You will soon get well. That will help you get as big as I am."

Tim did what Mick said for him to do. He sipped his milk. He ate his ham and eggs. He had fish and chicken, too. He ate all they told him to eat. Soon Tim was well. He got bigger each day.

Mick said, "Come here, Tim. Lift this fish. You can do it."

Tim lifted the fish. It was easy. He lifted a tub. It was not so easy. He lifted a basket of apples. Lifting was not easy. It was hard.

Mick said, "Let me see your fists, Tim. Soon you will have big fists like I have."

"That is OK, Mick. I am happy just the way I am now."

How old was Tim?
How old was Mick?
How big did Tim want to be?
Was Tim happy after he got well?

HANK, THE JESTER

Hank is a hunk of a man. He is a very fat jester when his pockets are full. His pants have big, big pockets in them. He can put lots of junk in them. Then he has to look for his junk. Hank digs in his pockets until he finds just what he wants. He fixes funny things just to make people laugh. That is why they call him the "jester".

Hank got an old wig and put it on a lamp. He walked back and winked at it. Then he put it on the stand and laughed. It did look funny.

Hank got a mask and put
it on an elephant's tusk.
He painted two red lips on
the tusk and got another
wig to put on the top.
Then he put it on the
stand beside the
old lamp.

The gang thinks Hank is a funny jester.
They like to see him make things so they can
laugh with him.

Who is Hank?
What did he do with the lamp?
What did he do with the elephant's tusk?
Why do people like him?

STAN'S BIG PANTS

Stan is a big man. He is a funny clown. Stan is a very thin clown. His pants have big pockets. Look at Stan's big pockets.

A clock will fit in this big pocket. Put a clam in this pocket. It will fit. Look at the drum and glove. This will fit in Stan's big pockets.

Here is a crutch. It will fit in a pocket. Put a hat and a wig in the pocket. This pan will fit, too.

The disk and mask will fit. Stan has a pink flag. This pink flag will fit. Stan put a clamp in his pocket. Then he put in a bag of sand. Look at the pockets now.

Stan said, "I will pick up six toy cars and put them in my pocket. They will fit."

Stan's puppy, Scamp, said, "Woof! Woof!"

"Look at Scamp," said Stan. "Scamp wants in the pocket, too."

That is all. The pockets are full. Look at Stan's pants now. Stan is a funny clown. Stan is not a thin clown now. Stan is a funny fat clown.

Who is Stan?
At first, what size was Stan?
What was the first thing Stan put in his pockets?
What was the last thing Stan put in his pockets?
What size was Stan at the end of the story?

PLANTING TIME

The time to plant the garden had come. Kim loved to play in the dirt. She told Mom she was going to make a flower garden.

They picked out the spot where Kim could plant her seeds. First, she had to dig the dirt to make it just perfect for planting. She made some little holes in the dirt so she could plant the seeds. Then she pushed the dirt over the top and planned to wait for her flowers.

In a few weeks, her plants came up and kept getting bigger and bigger. One day, Kim saw some very little yellow flowers on her plants. She called to Mom, "Come look at my flowers. They are little, but I think I will pick them."

Mom laughed, "Oh, Kim. Those are not flowers to pick. These flowers have to stay on the plant for a while. You must have picked up tomato seeds – not flower seeds."

"But they are flowers," said Kim.
"Your tomatoes are blooming. They
will turn into big tomatoes to eat in
about six weeks," said Mom.

What did Kim want to plant?
What did Kim have to do first to get ready
for a garden?
What did Kim want to do when she saw
the flowers?
What did Mom tell her about the flowers?

SPUD DOES TRICKS

Brad likes to teach his dog to do tricks. Spud is smart and can do lots of stunts. Brad tells Spud to sit up. Spud does it. Brad tells Spud to roll over, and over he goes.

Spud will run after a stick and bring it back to Brad. Spud can catch a Frisbie in the air. Brad has taught him to walk on his back legs and howl.

The best trick is when Brad gets a bit of raw meat and has Spud sit up. Spud holds the meat on his nose until Brad snaps his fingers.

Brad's pals brag about how smart Spud is. They think Spud should be in a circus to do his tricks.

What has Brad taught Spud to do?
What does he do when he gets a stick?
What does he do with a Frisbie?
What is Spud's best trick?

A TRAIN RIDE

Dave and Mike got
out of bed one morning.
"Look at the rain," said
Dave. "We can not go
to the lake today. It is
too cold to swim."

Mike said, "Let us wait and see what Dad says. He will be home at nine."

When Dad came home, he said, "There is too much rain to go to the lake. It is too cold to swim."

"What can we do?" said Dave. "We can not sail the boat."

Dad waited a little bit. Then he said, "I will use my brain. We can ride on the train and take a ride on the railroad."

"I like that," said Dave. "We can get out of the rain on the train."

"I like that, too. I like to ride on a train," said Mike. "Dad, you have a good brain."

Where had Mike and Dave planned to go in the morning?
Why could they not go to the lake?
What did they do when it rained?
What did Mike say about Dad?

THE SNAIL TRAIL

Blaine and Jane went for a walk on a trail to the lake. They saw six little quails. The babies walked in a line back of their mother. The mother quail had a long pretty tail.

The little quails had no tails at all. The little ones looked like buff balls the size of a nut. The quails walked to a chain gate on the trail.

Blaine and Jane saw a sign that said, STOP. Blaine said, "Let us wait here. I will use my brain and then I can tell you why they would put a STOP sign here.

Blaine sat down on a stump along the trail. He laid his hands on his head. Blaine said, "I think I know why the sign said, STOP. This is a snail and quail trail.

Jane said, "Let the quails and snails have this trail. We can take the main trail." "You have a good brain, too," said Blaine. "We can have more fun on the main trail."

How many baby quail did Blaine and Jane see?
What did the sign say?
Why was the sign put there?
Where did Jane and Blaine go?

DAN LEARNS TO PRINT

Dan had just started to school and loved to read. It was fun to sound out the letters and make words. He was so good at it. The other kids in the class did not see how he could be so smart. They would ask Dan to help them. He loved it.

Some of the time Dan looked sad. The teacher asked him what was the matter, "Nothing," said Dan. He did not want to tell her his printing was hard for him to do.

His best friend, Troy said, "Dan, I need a lot of help. Will you help me with my

reading, please? I would do any-
thing to help you. You can play
with cars and trains. You can use
my bike. I just need help."

That gave Dan an idea. "Yes,"
he said, "I will help you, but you
must help me do my printing. I
just can not print the letters."

"I think I know what is the
matter, Dan. You press too hard
with your pencil and do not follow
the tracks for the letters. No
wonder you are having trouble,"
said Troy.

"OK", said Dan. "I will try. This is going to be a good trade. I like this idea."

"This is a good trade for me, too." said Troy. "I think we make a good pair."

What did Dan do the best?
Why did he look sad sometimes?
Who asked him to help with the reading?
What was the trade the boys made?

A RIDE ON A SLED

Slim's family had just moved to a farm. It was winter and the snow started to come down. Slim had never lived where there was snow before. He did not know that it could get so cold.

Slim's new friend, Skipper, came to see him. "Let us go coasting down the hill. I have two sleds and you can have one of them. It is cold, but it will be fun," said Skipper.

Slim and Skipper bundled up with sweaters, scarves, hats, mittens and

snow boots. As Slim started out on the snow, his feet slipped out from under him. Down, down, he went. He slid to the bottom of the path.

Skipper laughed, "That is not the way to do it, Slim. You have to get on the sled and coast down the hill."

"OK, OK." laughed Slim. "That snow is slippery."

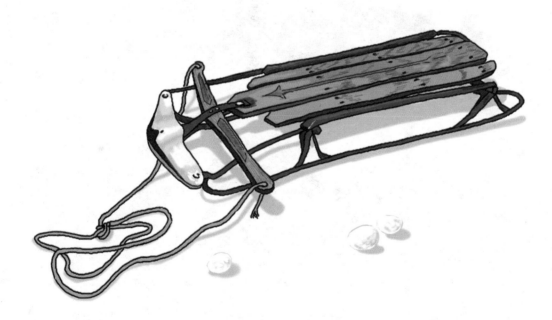

The boys pulled the sleds up the hill. They sat on the sleds, and away they went all the way down to the bottom.

"This is fun," said Slim. "Let us do it again. I am going to like living in a snow bank."

Where did Slim's family move?
What did Skipper want Slim to do with him?
What happened to Slim when he first went outside?
How did the boys spend their time?

SMELL THE ROSES

Jack went to the pet store to buy a puppy. Mr. Smith took Jack into the room where the puppies were kept in their cages. Jack looked at all of them. Then he saw one that really looked like something special.

This small puppy was a smoky-gray color. He was fuzzy with a pink nose that seemed to get into every corner. Jack told Mr. Smith, "This is the one I want. I will call him 'Smoky'."

Jack got Smoky home. Smoky sniffed at everything. He jumped on the coffee table and pushed two dishes off on the floor. The dishes smashed. Smoky sniffed and smelled at all the broken dishes.

"It looks as if you will need some training," said Jack. He smiled because Smoky was such a cute puppy. "Let us put you outside and see what you can find."

As soon as Smoky was outside, he ran to the bed of flowers and smelled them. He was just about to smell one of the roses when a bee landed on the same rose. Smoky kept smelling

the roses until .... Just then Smoky let out a howl. Smoky backed up and ran to Jack, howling all the way.

Jack said, "Smoky, I do not think you will be smelling the roses any more."

Where did Jack get Smoky?
What color was Smoky?
What did Smoky do when he first got in the house?
What happened when Smoky got outside?

WHAT IS THAT NOISE?

Sam woke up one night. He heard a noise. What could it be? He snuggled down under the quilts and covered his head. What was it?

Sam listened again. The noise was louder. He sniffed the air to see if he could smell  smoke. No, that noise did not come from a fire. Sam snapped his fingers to see if he was really awake. Yes. The noise was getting louder.

Sam tiptoed down the steps. He snagged his slipper on the step, but that did not stop him. He had to find out what that noise was.

Sam slipped very quietly into the kitchen. No, the noise was not in here. He tiptoed into the living room. No, the noise was not here. He crawled closer to Dad and Mom's bedroom. Oh, Oh! The noise was louder.

Sam slammed the door open and yelled, "Dad, Mom, there is a noise in our house!" Dad sat up in bed. The noise stopped. Sam laughed. "Oh, Dad. Now I know what the noise was. You were snoring. How can you sleep with all that noise?"

Where was Sam when he heard the noise?
What did he think it might be?
Where did he look first?
What was making the noise?

THE FUZZY RUNT

"I know the one I want," yelled Scott. "This is going to be my puppy."

Dad said, "Are you sure you want this one, Scott? He is the runt of the bunch. He is so fuzzy. The other puppies are much bigger."

"I am sure," said Scott. "I will take good care of him. I promise. Let us go show Mom."

When Mom saw the puppy, she said, "He's cute. But, he is kind of a runt?"

"Oh, Mom, do not say that," said Scott. "He may be little now, but he will not always be a runt. I will take good care of him," Scott promised. "I will call him 'Little Gus' now."

Scott fixed a bed for the puppy. Little Gus slept much of the time. Scott played with his friends. While Scott was gone, Little Gus woke up. He was hungry. He looked in his pan for some milk and food. The pan was empty.

Little Gus went into the kitchen. He sniffed around for something to eat. No food was there. He went to the porch and found the cat's dish of food. He sniffed it. It did not smell too good. After all, Little Gus was hungry so he ate the cat's food.

About that time, Old Tom Cat saw what Little Gus had done. He did not like that one bit. He went over to Little Gus and gave him a big slap and a smack with his paw. Little Gus howled and cried.

Scott heard Little Gus howling. He ran in the house and saw what had happened. Little Gus had a bloody nose and scratches on his back.

Scott picked him up. "I am sorry, Little Gus," he said. "I did not think to leave some puppy food and milk for you. I will take better care of you."

Little Gus wagged his tail. Scott said, "You are Little Gus now, but if I take good care of you, soon you will be Big Gus."

What did Dad think about the puppy?
What did Scott call the puppy?
Why did the puppy get a bloody nose and scratches?
What did Scott promise to do?

A NEAT CHAIN

Each year Jean's family went to Seal Beach. Grandma lived near the sea.

Jean loved to walk with Grandma along the beach.

Jean picked up pretty little rocks and shells. She put them in her pocket. When they got home, she got them out and looked at them. They were as pretty as beads.

Grandma said, "Let us get a chain. We can make a shell and rock chain that will be as neat as a chain of beads."

Jean put the chain around her neck. Jean liked the shell and rock chain better than any other chain she had.

"Thanks, Grandma," said Jean. "You are a neat Grandma."

Where did Jean's family go?
Where did Jean walk with her Grandma?
What did she find?
What did Grandma do with them?

PEE WEE

The Greek queen was a sweet queen. She had pretty pink cheeks and a deep smile. People were always happy to speak to her.

It was time for her speech. She took three steps to peek at the staff. Then she began to speak.

"I want you to seek a little kitten for me. It must have soft feet. I hope it has good teeth. It can be yellow or black," she said.

The staff wanted to seek the kitten the queen needed.

Gene had a kitten that was white. No, that would not keep the queen happy.

Gail had a kitten that was too big. She said, "The queen wants a little kitten." This big kitten will not keep the queen happy.

Jane saw a kitten that was little. It had soft feet. It had good teeth. The kitten was all black. "I feel the queen will like this kitten," Jane said.

Jane went to greet the queen. "Here is your little kitten," she said.

The queen took a peek at the kitten. "This is the kitten I need," said the queen. "This kitten is little. It has soft feet. It has good teeth. This kitten is all black. I will call him 'Pee Wee' because he is so little and soft. He can sleep in his bed beside me. Thank you, Jane. You gave me Pee Wee."

What color kitten did the queen want?
What kind of feet did she want for the kitten?
What kitten did Gail find for the queen?
Who got the kitten the queen needed?
What did the queen call the kitten?

THE QUILT

Beth and her family had moved into a new house in the town of Quim. Their house was big, and Beth had a bedroom of her own. Always before she had shared one with her sister, Ruth. Now she had a room where she could have her own clothes, her own desk, her own bed, her own closet, her own chair, and her own books. She was happy.

Mom told the girls she would make a quilt for each of their beds. The catch was that the one who kept her room the neatest would get the first quilt.

121

Beth and Ruth said, "That is fair. We will both try to get the first one."

Every morning Beth made her bed and kept her clothes picked up and put in the closet. Sometimes, Ruth forgot. Every morning Beth kept her books on the shelves. Sometimes, Ruth forgot.

Mom finished making the first quilt. It matched the colors in Beth's room. Mom said, "Beth, you are the one who kept your room the neatest. You get the first quilt."

"Thanks, Mom," said Beth. "I love it. It makes my room so nice. You were so quick to get it done. Thanks, Mom."

Ruth looked at the pretty quilt. "I think I will keep my room neater after this. I want a pretty quilt, too. I will try, Mom. I will do it," she said.

Where did Beth's family move?
What did Mom promise to do for the girls?
How did Beth keep her room?
Who got the first quilt?